A Cake for Dave

by Liza Charlesworth

ISBN: 978-1-338-84439-9

Art Director: Tannaz Fassihi; Designer: Cynthia Ng; Illustrated by Michael Robertson

3 4 5 6 68 26 25 24

Printed in Jiaxing, China. First printing, June 2022.

SCHOLASTIC

"Dave is ten!" said Kate.
"I can make him a cake."

Mix, mix, mix.
Bake, bake, bake.
Ice, ice, ice!

"It is late," said Kate.
"I need to take Dave
his cake."

Kate saw Dave's pal
Wade at a lake.
Wave, wave!

"Dave is ten!" said Kate.
"I can take him a game,"
said Wade.

Kate saw Dave's pal
Jane at a gate.
Wave, wave.

"Dave is ten!" said Kate.
"I can take him a vase,"
said Jane.

Kate, Wade, and Jane
ran to a big cave.
Race, race, race!

"DAVE, DAVE, DAVE!"
said Kate, Wade, and Jane.

Dave came out of his big cave.
Dave is an ape!
Dave has a cape!

Wade gave Dave a game.
Jane gave Dave a vase.
Kate gave Dave a cake.

Then Dave and his pals
ate and ate and ate!

Read & Review

Invite your learner to point to each long-*a* word and read it aloud.

Dave
cake
late

cape
wave
make

gave
came
Wade

ape
game
race

Jane
bake
vase

Fun Fill-Ins

Read the sentences aloud, inviting your learner to complete them using the long-*a* words in the box.

game ape cave vase cake

1. Kate gave Dave a ________.
2. Wade gave Dave a ________.
3. Jane gave Dave a ________.
4. Dave lives in a ________.
5. Dave is an ________!